Christopher Cartier of Hazelnut, also known as Bear

Antonine
MAILLET

Christopher Cartier of Hazelnut, also known as Bear

TRANSLATED BY

Wayne Grady

Methuen

Toronto   New York   London   Sydney   Auckland

Canadian Cataloguing in Publication Data

Maillet, Antonine, 1929–
    [Christophe Cartier de la noisette dit Nounours. English].
    Christopher Cartier of Hazelnut, also known as Bear

Translation of: Christophe Cartier de la noisette dit Nounours.
ISBN 0-458-98110-9

I. Title.   II. Title: Christophe Cartier de la noisette dit Nounours.   English.

PS8562.A54C4713 1984   C843'.54   C84-099163-0
PQ3919.2.M26C4713 1984

Lines quoted from *The Fables of Jean de La Fontaine*, translated into English verse by Edward Marsh (London: William Heinemann Ltd., 1933), are reprinted by permission of William Heinemann Limited.

Printed and bound in the United States

1 2 3 4 5   84   89 88 87 86 85

To my childhood neighbour,
Alice Goguen, who told me my first story,
about Goldilocks and the Three Bears.
Now, half a century later, Bear says thanks.

I

*W*hen I met Bear I was living in my lighthouse by the ocean, stuck in the sand like a fencepost, surrounded by boats and nets and fishermen's sons and seagulls and seaweed and seashells. It was a beautiful lighthouse, with a tower and lamps to light the way for lost sailors, except that it didn't light the way for lost sailors because it wasn't a real lighthouse. It was an out-of-service lighthouse. Some day, mark my words, we'll need lighthouses again, and I'll have myself declared Keeper of My Own Lighthouse, and my lighthouse will be a real lighthouse, once and for all.

At least that's what I used to tell myself. But before that happened I met Bear.

I used to go for walks along the beach every morning to gather rubies. I knew that they weren't real rubies, that real rubies mostly inhabit the Gaspé and that the rubies I gathered on my beach were really pebbles. I knew that. At first it used to bother me when they told me that my red and blue and purple pebbles weren't rubies, but I told myself that sooner or later the sea would back up and change direction and the currents would come north-south instead of south-east, and that when that happened real rubies would wash down on my beach.

That was before I met Bear.

Sometimes I went out in my boat. It wasn't a big boat like the fishermen used; it didn't have a cabin and a keel and a rudder. My boat was more what you'd call a rowboat. I couldn't take it too far out, either, because of the currents, and the north-east wind that would come up suddenly without warning. So I stayed inside the spits. That way, I thought, if something happened I could always save myself by climbing out onto a spit.

Spit, that's a funny word. After I met Bear he told me that they weren't really *my* spits, that they... But I'll get to that later.

First I have to tell you that I only live in my lighthouse during the season. The lighthouse season. The other three seasons are the city season, the farming season, and the forest season. Oh, and there's the sugaring-off season, and the berry-picking season, too, but around a lighthouse you don't find a lot of blueberries or maple trees. Only dune grass. And here and there a daisy, but it would have to be a very brave daisy, and it wasn't a very good place for them. The slightest breeze from the east would cover their petals with millions of grains of salt, and that would kill them right dead. That's why you have to transplant daisies every year if you want them to grow around a lighthouse, because of the salt winds. Of course, anyone listening to daisies out in the fields would think that my daisies weren't real daisies.

But I'll tell you one thing, I know someone who could make a sandy lighthouse yard look like a grassy meadow!

One day, it was a year ago today, I left my lighthouse as usual to go for a walk along the beach to collect rubies. The wind was up, and I remember saying to myself that the daisies were in for a hard time. I had already put up stakes for the most fragile ones, and I suppose I should have staked up the rest of them, but after all! I couldn't spend all my time looking after daisies, could I? I couldn't go devoting my whole life to them, waiting on them and waiting on them, day after day, waiting for the wind to die down and the sea to back up and the rocks to rise up out of the water to make my lighthouse a lighthouse again. Enough was enough!

I turned away from the beach and entered the woods.

And that's how I came to meet Christopher Cartier of Hazelnut, also known as Bear. That day all the trees in the forest were acting completely crazy. The poplars, the hazelnut trees, the beeches, the oaks, the white birch, all of them, all babbling and stammering, all quite drunk: there's no other word for it, they were drunk. With little streams working at their roots, and little springs tickling their bark, and moss and ivy and acorns and dead leaves that were only pretending to be dead. The forest was so drunk it was stivvering—oops! Excuse me, that's one of our words. I used it because it was the favourite word of one of my uncles, who used to stivver all the time because it's such a funny word. My uncle used to come out and say whatever came into his head. When a drunk man stivvers it means he zigs and zags, and get out of his way, because he might try to step on your toes.

Anyway, that day the trees were stivvering and staggering and reeling back and forth as if they'd all had too much sparkling wine. I was scandalized, I can tell you, and I was clucking my tongue like this: *tsk tsk tsk,* when I heard a kind of *psssst!* coming up from the moss under my feet. I looked down and saw a procession of ants, all lined up in a row Indian style, heading off toward an unknown destination. I'm not normally a very curious or indiscreet person, you understand, but I do like to know what's brewing up around me. So I told myself I would join the column. Have you ever tried to find the tail end of a column of ants? You haven't? Well, take it from me, a column of ants does not have a tail. It doesn't have a head, either, for that matter: it is a totally indeterminable procession of foolishness. I decided to throw myself into the ranks.

And came nose to muzzle with none other than Christopher Cartier of Hazelnut, also known as Bear.

I've tried many times since then to find out if he took his name from Jacques Cartier or from Christopher Columbus, but there was no finding out from him. He was just called Christopher Cartier after the most famous explorer in the world—in *his* world, that is, Bear's world. When I tried to tell him that *his* world was also *my* world and a whole lot of other people's world as well, and that Jacques Cartier and Christopher Columbus lived at least forty years apart and could not possibly be one and the same person, well, he just put on his most offended, his most stubborn manner, and let me know in no uncertain terms that *he* knew what he was talking about if no one else did. In fact, I often wondered if...

But there I am, getting ahead of myself again. It's still too early to start climbing the Hazelnut tree. Because that day, the day of my famous walk in the woods, the day of the zigzag of ants into which I had thrust myself, the day I stumbled into that patch of low underbrush, I knew nothing at all about the highly imaginative character of my new friend Bear, otherwise known as Christopher Cartier of Hazelnut.

But I was soon going to find out.

It was around noon—I remember because of the sun. At the end of September, just like at the middle of May, the sun is very dangerous because of its infrared rays. Bear called them Winnifred rays, but I know he sometimes used to trip over his own tongue, and that what he really meant to say was infrared. The

Winni...er, infrared rays in September, as I was saying, must have heated up the tree sap more than usual, because the whole forest was in a strangely agitated mood. It was weird.

It wasn't just that everyone was talking at the same time. You couldn't really call it talking, even: it was screeching, miaowing, croaking, chirping, yelping, yapping, chittering, cooing, warbling—an unbelievable cacophony. I felt like shouting, "Whoa, not so fast, not so loud, I can't understand a word!" But no one would have heard me. As a matter of fact, though I don't like to admit it, no one seemed to have noticed my presence at all. We like to think we're pretty important sometimes...Anyway, no one was paying the slightest attention to me. But the fact remains that on that day, in that patch of underbrush, some very strange things were going on. It was a kind of universal suspension of the laws of Nature.

Bear always refused to talk to me about it, hiding his voice behind a fit of coughing, or a long, drawn-out sneeze, whenever I broached the subject. But I had a good idea that if the whole underbrush was in such a hullabaloo that afternoon it was because someone, and I won't mention any names, had got them going. And if I wanted to I could point my finger at the one person in the crowd who seemed so adamant about not discussing the matter.

But never mind for now. At the very heart of the forest that September day, Christopher Cartier was laying down the law to an assemblage of rabbits, weasels, badgers, groundhogs, squirrels, partridges, ants, foxes, screech-owls, and skunks—the whole aristocracy of the forest, in fact. And there was Bear, sitting on his silky bottom, as he would say—though of course he *wouldn't* say it—reading the riot act to the whole pack of rascals (he *would* say that!) and

5

telling them that they'd better come clean or else. Of course you realize that I'm reporting this in Bear's own words.

Like you, I raised an eyebrow at those words "pack of rascals." I couldn't help it; I asked myself what those words could possibly mean in the mouth of a little bear cub who was talking to a group of adults. But there he was, speaking down his nose to a portly, dressed-for-business skunk and a venerable, worldly-wise old hare. He was shouting at them, in fact, making a speech, raising his paw in the air to emphasize his point of view, trying every way he knew to impose his interpretation of things on the rest of the underbrush. And they were taking it.

I must have gone *tsk tsk* again, or maybe I chuckled, I don't remember now, but I do remember, as a fisherman remembers his own cove, that Christopher Cartier a.k.a. Bear lifted his head, wrinkled his whole face around his snout in order to see me better, and buried his eyes deeply into mine. For three full seconds—I counted them—we measured each other up and down, and in the end it was Bear who lowered his gaze. He tried to pretend it was on account of the Winnifred rays (he repeated Winnifred twice to let me know he wasn't an ignoramus who couldn't tell a Winnifred from an infrared), but I rather think he was disconcerted to be meeting a human gaze for the first time. He even tried to camouflage his discomfort by making a series of faces and pirouetting about to amuse his friends. But he couldn't fool the old rabbit, or the owl, or the fox, who was always grinning in that way foxes have. They must have known, especially the weasel, that all Bear's antics were only meant to hide the fact that something serious had occurred.

What they didn't suspect, though, was that Bear had made a decision.

I didn't suspect it myself, to tell the truth. I took a last look at the group and tiptoed out of the underbrush: the last thing I saw was Master Hazelnut, who had the colossal nerve, the brazen effrontery, to turn around and stick his behind at this example of retreating humankind. I shrugged my shoulders and smiled—it was a splendid gesture, after all—and went off in search of my column of ants. Before I knew it I was back on the forest path.

II

I had been walking briskly
for several quarters of an hour, three or four at least,
and was just about to leave the forest when I thought I
heard a kind of puffing sound, hardly more than a
whisper, coming up behind me. I looked to my right,
then to my left. The trees seemed to have calmed
down—they were breathing, all right, but they
weren't panting. The sound must have been coming
from somewhere else.

I started walking again. This time I heard footsteps.
There was no getting around it, I could definitely hear
someone following me. I tried to ignore it. I even tried
laughing out loud, because when you're in the middle
of the forest you never know, you know. But laugh or
no laugh, I had my doubts. And in situations like that,
doubts can be much worse than plain old ordinary
fear. After all, I had been brought up to face things
face to face.

Face to face? How could I face this thing face to
face, when the thing that was facing me when I turned
around was not a face at all, but the silky little bottom
of a bear?

At least this time I could see that he wasn't doing it
on purpose to annoy me. He was trying to run away
from me. Very quickly. And when a bear cub tries to
run away from you, as you will notice if you ever find
yourself in my neck of the woods, he always shows you
his worst part.

"Hey!" someone shouted, and I was very surprised to find out it was me. I had done it without thinking. The "Hey!" had just come out all by itself. Who knows why? Sometimes we just do things, make certain gestures, say certain words, have certain reactions, that seem to come out of nowhere, out of some dark, hidden corner of ourselves. From our kidneys, maybe, or from our heart, I don't know. But I do know that this time it changed my life.

"Hey you! Where do you think you're off to?"

He stopped, sort of froze in mid-stride with his front legs back behind his back legs, a trick only bears can pull off—and kangaroos, I suppose, and rabbits, and maybe beavers, and I guess squirrels and monkeys. Come to think of it, any animal whose hind legs are longer than its front legs. Bear was quite put out later on when I told him that I had included monkeys in my list of animals that had certain characteristics in common with bears.

"Monkeys," he said. "Pouah!"

I didn't dare tell him about the monkey I'd seen one day in a circus. He had been imitating a bear, and he had the whole audience rolling in the aisles with laughter. It made me wonder why one half of the world spends its time mocking the other half, and the other half is busy laughing at the first half, which is...anyway, we were both wrong: monkeys have front legs that are longer than their hind legs. And if a monkey can ape the antics of a bear or a squirrel or a rabbit or some other short-front-legged creature, it's because it's...well, it's an ape.

"Was that you making all that fuss back there in the underbrush?"

He turned around at that and gave me a withering look. Then he got embarrassed. I guess he hadn't expected me to come right out with it, and had turned around more or less in spite of himself. A reflex action that came from his kidneys, perhaps, or his heart. But he had turned around, and he couldn't take it back now. He either had to answer me or—no, he had to answer me, come what may. So he answered just any old thing:

"We were having a little discussion about stars," he said.

"Stars? What stars?"

"Oh, Aldebaran, you know. And Betelgeuse."

Betelgeuse! My my, wasn't he a brassy one, though? Brassy about stars, at any rate, if he could rhyme off names like Aldebaran and Betelgeuse. I knew a thing or two about stars myself, and I found it hard to believe that forest people could be as well acquainted with their behaviour as I was. In my experience there are two kinds of people who know nothing about stars: city people and forest people. City people because they make so much noise all the time and have so many street lights that they put the stars right out, make them shut right up! And forest people because stars are hidden from them by a ceiling of trees.

But I had often heard my father say that nothing stays hidden from those who wish to find it. I could go along with my father on that, I suppose, except that I would have thought it made more sense to begin looking for something a little bit closer to home and a little bit more useful than stars. What in the world would a bear want with a star?

"It's a family matter," he added, with the air of someone who has relatives scattered about from here to Peru.

"A family matter," I repeated, to make sure I'd got it right.

"You've heard of the Great Bear, haven't you?"

He had me there. When you bear the names of the two greatest explorers in the world, and when you have Hazelnut blood running in your veins, you could very easily be descended from stars.

It occurred to me that the best thing for me to do was to get out of the forest, fast, if I didn't want to fall into the clumsiest of all bear traps—which is to get caught up in a long, endless argument about nothing at all just to increase Bear's own self-esteem. So I told him that if he wanted to argue he might as well go back to his clearing in the underbrush and argue with someone much more naïve or much more obstinate than I was. And I took to my heels.

Thus ending, cleanly and with no hard feelings, the shortest friendship that fate had yet thrown in my path.

Or so I thought.

Because I was to learn that fate is much more stubborn and much more far-sighted than we are. And, when it comes right down to it, much more generous. If I'd been left to my own devices that day I'd have lost Bear. He was the stubborn one, drawn along perhaps by his own private star, the Great Bear. When I had left the forest and was making my way across the wheatfield, I once again became aware of a puffing sound, and the rustle of little silk paws in the ripening wheat.

This time, though, I didn't turn around. What was the use? I knew he was following me, and I knew I couldn't stop him. It was too late: once a bear cub, who is about the size of a poodle, sticks his nose out of the forest for the first time, you can't just send him packing. He wouldn't be able to find his way back, for one thing. It was very reckless of him to follow me, and I was tempted to tell him so. But I think he already knew it, because the faster I walked with my big, human-sized steps, first through the wheat, then through some hay, and finally out into the dune grass near the shore, the faster he galloped behind me, as if he was afraid of being left alone and finding himself suddenly smack dab in the middle of civilization.

So I took pity on him.

"You again," I said, without raising my voice.

He lowered his eyes. But then he raised them—he did have his pride, after all. And when it comes to a contest between pride and fear, pride always wins out. Especially in bears. And I suppose it's the same with any other creature that comes from prehistoric times. Otherwise they never would have come from pre-historic times.

"Do you know the sea?" I asked him, knowing full well he could only answer No.

"Yes," he said.

When he saw my jaw drop he tried to distract me by launching into a long description of an old lake that was hidden away in the woods, called Lake Molasses. If I'd let him go on he'd have started talking about swamps and marshes too, but I cut him off before his tongue had a chance to run away with him.

"That's the sea over there," I said, and I lifted him up to my shoulder height and pointed him in the direction of the sea, which was cooing up to the foot of my lighthouse.

I felt something go thump against his ribs. His heart, I thought to myself; even a bear can have feelings, and can be moved by the beauty of the ocean. But I was wrong, it wasn't that. Bear's first glimpse of the sea's infinite emptiness had inspired more terror in him than admiration. You must have noticed it yourself, how it's often the things and the people we love most who are most able to fill us with fear and trembling.

When I put him back down on terra firma, he went down on all fours as if he knew I wasn't going to run away and leave him. He trotted along beside me with his snout in the air, and headed straight for my lighthouse as if he'd never lived anywhere else in his life. I watched him as he pranced boldly along, his little silk bottom wagging back and forth like an archbishop's surplice on Confirmation Day. In fact, he looked so funny that I said to myself—

"Where's the lamp?" Bear asked suddenly, interrupting my thoughts.

"The lamp?"

"The lamp, yes. It's a lighthouse, isn't it? It's supposed to have a lamp on it to show the way for seagulls and larks who are lost."

"Oh, *that* lamp," I said. "It's...er, it's being fixed."

"Good. You better hurry it up, though. The seagulls might die."

I couldn't believe my ears. Where the devil had this little bear cub learned about lighthouses and lamps and seagulls?

"You know about lighthouses?" I asked him.

He made five or six knowing faces and nodded his head wisely a few times instead of answering my question, then he tried to change the subject. But I wasn't going to let him off the hook.

"Where did you learn about lighthouses?" I insisted.

He squirmed a bit, but in the end I found out that in the forest they often talked at great length and in great detail about thousands of things they knew nothing about, usually repeating stories they'd heard from migrating birds. Once a great flock of Canada geese had stopped for a rest on Lake Molasses, and they had told tales of a lighthouse they had passed somewhere that lit up the way for seagulls, and seeing my lighthouse had reminded Bear of their stories.

Christopher Cartier of Hazelnut, I said to myself, you may not know very much about very many things, but you have a pretty good head on your shoulders.

And I told him he could spend the night under my lighthouse porch.

III

*T*hat night I slept like a bear, and I dreamed of a land where the rivers flowed with milk and honey. And when I woke up at dawn I had only one memory—my tower—and one thought: to go up into it to dirty my usual number of clean sheets of paper. I got out of bed and slipped on my slacks, stretching out my whole body with joy at the smell of the salty, early morning air. The sea lay muffled in fog, but by ten o'clock it would be clear and fine. Time enough to cut up a few oranges into little boats for carrying water to my mouth, to make some fresh coffee, and—

But what was all that racket coming up from the beach? And on such a fine morning?

Believe it or not, I had forgotten all about my excursion into the forest, and my subsequent meeting with Bear. It had gone completely out of my head. Don't worry, though: it was the last time I'd be allowed to forget, even for a moment, the existence of that little whirlwind who had come blustering into my life. Bear was not one to let me forget about him a second time.

I ran out onto the porch, grabbing a skillet by the tail as I went in order to have something to use to defend the poor forest creature I had dragged (though against my will) out of his natural habitat. Uninvited or not, he was still my guest, and anyone who attacked him was attacking me.

"Bear! Bear!" I shouted as I ran. Maybe you've noticed how, in moments of extreme tragedy or urgency, people always go immediately to the point. Which is why in this case I didn't waste time trying to call Bear by all his Christian and family names.

"Bear!"

I brandished my frying pan and made a rush at the air force that seemed to have made a prisoner of my little friend. Twenty-two or thirty-six seabirds were fluttering and chattering about on the shore, the whole morning beachful of them, seagulls and larks and sawbills and even a few crows, who looked like black specks in that brilliant circle of whiteness. Poor Bear! All I could see of him was a little furry patch amid a swarm of webbed feet and wings and beaks and bills. They all seemed to be pecking the daylights out of him.

"Bear!" I sobbed.

I needn't have bothered, you know. I had misjudged my gulls and the other shore birds. When I got close enough I saw that young Master Hazelnut was merely sitting on his little silk butt on the sand, calmly recounting to his audience the story of how he got his name. The squawking and nattering I had mistaken for a pitched battle was nothing more than a somewhat lively discussion of genealogy. In all my years of living on the coast, which had been quite a few, almost my whole life, I had never heard a flock of shore birds—it was Bear who later called them my fowl-weather friends—who could discuss *anything* at all without turning the discussion into something that resembled a full-scale war. But like you, I guess, I still had a lot to learn.

One thing I learned that day was that the names of all the important families in the area—the Pleo-nasms, the Featherstones, the Hockneys—all harked back to the sayings and deeds of their ancestors. The Hockneys, for example, are the direct descendants of the groundhog, who, upon seeing his own shadow on Groundhog Day, played hockney from school and was afraid to go back home, so he turned the calendar back and gave us forty days of good weather in the middle of winter. That's one thing I learned. Another was that the Featherstones got their name from their ancestor the skunk, commonly called the little stinker, who did his business with such enthusiasm one day that he turned a wild turkey into solid rock. And ever since that day a stone feather has been emblazoned on the family crest. As for the Pleonasms, their name speaks for itself.

But the name that interested me most was Hazelnut. I must have asked him twenty times about his background, and each time he sent me away from the well with an empty bucket—or with blank pages. After ten times I was astonished; after fifteen I was perplexed; the twentieth time I asked myself whether or not Christopher Cartier was trying to hide something from me.

Today, though, I believe that the true truth is that he wanted to be able to keep dreaming, and so he refused to pin down his past once and for all. You know how marvellous it is to be of that age when you can dream about your future—when you're under six, or over eighty, depending on the length of your future and the size of your dream. But imagine being able to dream about your past! Everything is possible, everything is permissible, because the past is completely without limits. You can never be bored with yourself. And that's what Bear wanted. Of course, he'll always run into people who won't appreciate his way of viewing things, and he'll have to explain to them that the real reality—

"Prrrt!"

That was Bear. As I was saying, for him the real reality—

"Prrrrrrt!"

Well! The rude thing! Those comments weren't coming from his mouth, in case you were wondering. They were coming from somewhere between his paws. No doubt about it, I said to myself, I still had a *lot* to learn.

I also told myself that I had more important things to do than go clambering up Bear's family tree. First I had to install Bear in my household at a level appropriate to his rank, which in my opinion was at the very bottom. Not that I'm a racist, or an elitist, or even a feudalist. It's just that I believe every creature has its appointed place in creation. The seagulls and larks belong on the shore; the sand dunes are the proper place for dune grass; the bottom of the ocean is just right for crabs; and under my porch is the perfect place for a bear cub who, of his own free will, has left his natural home in the forest in order to find out about the world. But just because you're at the bottom of the totem pole doesn't mean you're in any way inferior. It's just a matter of size and convenience: Bear was the only one at the lighthouse who could squeeze under the porch and feel more or less at home there.

I had to explain that to him, of course. It wasn't easy. Every time I used the words "rank" and "lower level" it made his fur stand on end.

Touchy, that's what he was.

To save face, he said he would sleep in my flower bed. But that turned out to be more complicated than he thought. Daisies have their pride, too. "My petals!" they cried out in their shrill little voices. "Can't you see you're hurting our feelings!" they squealed. "Didn't anyone ever teach you any manners!"

I was afraid Bear would be so insulted by that that he'd tear up those daisies with one swipe of his bear paw. I thought I was getting a pretty good idea of his wild and woolly nature. But I was wrong again. Instead, he bent down and gently kissed the flowers, then carefully removed his paws from their petals. A well-bred, truly noble person does not attack a daisy. What good would it do? And how could he go about telling people of his heroic exploits in the forest, or about his great plans for the future? Everyone would just say, Oh yeah, he's the guy who attacks daisies. How could he unburden his heart of its great sorrow, or show a sudden surge of tenderness? And Bear knew by instinct that he was stronger and more intelligent than a daisy, that he could overlook their insolence without losing dignity himself. In other words, Bear could treat the daisies the same way I was treating him.

I was learning a lot that day, wasn't I?

I'm not saying that I was naturally stronger than Bear. Just that it was a matter of our age difference. And as for intelligence, it really depended on what we were talking about. For instance, take the story of the herons. I haven't told you about the herons yet because I haven't had a chance—Bear seems to have taken over my past, my future, and my present, and I've been trying to put this story into some kind of order, to establish some priorities. I wanted it to begin at the beginning, for example, with the birth of my hero, then go on to describe his first steps, his first word, his family origins, what his father did for a living, what social level they occupied, their economic situation. I *wanted* to do it that way, but I couldn't.

And I have to say that it was Bear's fault, really. Every time I settled down to get serious and orderly he'd come romping in to upset my plans and throw a monkey-wrench into my priorities.

That's why I haven't had a chance to tell you about Bear's adventure with the herons yet.

It happened very early one morning. It had to happen then, because if you ever want to find out anything about herons you have to get up pretty early, no two ways about it. They don't hang around waiting for you. In fact, they won't even care if you never show up at all. The coast has never seen a more solitary, self-sufficient bird than the heron. You can see for yourself: get up on your tiptoes, if you happen to live in a lighthouse or something similar, go over to the window, and take a look at the seven or eight herons—never more than that—who are standing stiff-legged and quite apart from each other, looking as though they were perfectly prepared to wait forever for the sky to realize its duty and come down to serve them breakfast. And if you open the window or go out onto the porch, they won't even look up— their noses are already high enough, anyway—they won't so much as turn their heads to look at you. But with a beautiful, stately grace they will lift their whole bodies into the air, just like that, slowly fading out of your vision as if to say that it was you and you alone who had disturbed their peace of mind.

Herons are like that.

So you can imagine what it was like one fine morning when Christopher Cartier of Hazelnut, who had never seen a heron in his life before, decided he would go out hunting them. I'll spare you the details of the riot that ensued. But, to be fair, if Bear had never seen a heron before it was equally true that the herons had never seen a bear, either.

22

Who was this bold and reckless intruder? they must have asked themselves. Who asked him to come here like this, barging in on us uninvited? What a slap in the face! Never in living bird-memory has there been such a humiliating incident. Disturbed—nay, invaded!—during our morning meditations, when lesser creatures were supposed to be in Church. What unseemly behaviour from Sir Kill-Joy.

That, at least, was the herons' side of the story. Bear, as you might have guessed, had his own version.

"Did you see those herons?" he demanded. "It's not enough for them to waddle about on *our* beach as if they owned it. Oh no. It's not enough for them to turn their noses up at our common old carp and pike. But to refuse the hand of friendship when it is offered to them! To turn their backs on us and show us their hind-feathers!"

Poor Bear. He must have forgotten already that the first time I saw *him* he was doing exactly the same thing to me.

Then he added, with a knowing air: "If they don't watch it they'll end up eating snails."

I tried to hide my astonishment: Bear, who was hardly a day out of the forest, was quoting one of the fables of La Fontaine!

"What was that?" I asked as casually as I could.

But all Bear did was shake his head. I could see I'd have to push him a bit.

"Bear," I asked, "where did you hear that fable of La Fontaine?"

"Laugh on *who?*" he said, then bit his tongue: more than anything else in the world, Bear hated to appear ignorant. "Oh," he said quickly, "you mean Laugh on *Tayne*." But it was too late; he'd already shown me that he had never read the fables of La Fontaine. But then where in the world had he learned the story of

23

the heron and the snails? As a kind of test to see how much he did know, I began to recite "The Heron" as if it was the sort of thing everybody knew:

On his long legs the Heron, with his long bill
Handled by his long neck, sedately stalked...

And, to my complete amazement, I heard Bear take up the poem:

...Beside a river's marge he walked.

You could have knocked me down with a heron-feather! Bear? Reciting poetry? "Who taught you that?" I asked him.

"My father."

"And who taught it to your father?"

"His own father, of course!"

From father to son, I thought: no kidding! "Do you know the rest of the fable?"

This time he didn't bother to try to hide his ignorance. He was in too much of a hurry to learn something new.

"Fable?" he repeated. "What's a fable?"

"But you were just reciting one," I said:

On his long legs the Heron, with his long bill
Handled by his long neck, sedately stalked,
Beside a river's marge he walked.

"Oh, that," said Bear. "That's just an old story I learned when I was still a cub. I know another one, too:

My Lady Weasel one fine day
When Jack the Rabbit was away

24

Herself and all her household goods installs
(The artful thing!) in his ancestral halls.

And here's another:

One fine evening the Town Mouse
Asked the Country Mouse to dine
In a fash-i-onable house
Off remains of Valentine."

"Off what?" I asked.

He said "Valentine" again instead of "galantine"—
his first literary faux-pas—and I had to smile. But on
the inside, so as not to hurt his feelings.

"Is that what your ancestors used to do?" I asked
him. "Hand down stories about animals from father
to son?"

"Of course," he said. "What's wrong with stories
about animals?"

He had me there. There's nothing wrong with
stories about animals.

"That Laugh on Tayne guy who told them to you,"
he went on. "He must have got them from us."

So much for La Fontaine! Bear had just reduced him
to the status of a plagiarist, which is little better than a
liar. Or a little worse. In fact, Bear had made all
literature out to be a mere tributary of nature,
implying at the same time that oral literature was
truer than written literature. It quite took my breath
away.

Without knowing exactly why, I took Christopher
Cartier, alias Bear, in my arms and hugged him as
hard as I could.

IV

*W*hether it was my show of friendship, or whether it was being reminded of his grandfather and his fables about the Cat, the Weasel, and the Rabbit, I don't know. But whatever it was, Bear was suddenly plunged into a reminiscent mood, and before you could say "Jack Robinson" he had lifted a tiny corner of the curtain that hid his innermost secret of secrets.

Secrets? Bear?

Well sure, why not? Bear wasn't still wearing diapers, you know—all right, all right, bears don't wear diapers, they wear furry silk pajamas, I know, and I had to explain to Bear that "still wearing diapers" was just an expression, like "still wet behind the ears," a metaphor. Bear said he didn't like metaphors. He said metaphors were falling stars, and he had relatives up on Ursus Major and he didn't like stars that wouldn't stay up in their rightful places, and—

"I think you're talking about *meteors*," I interrupted.

But you try untangling Bear's tongue once he gets it wrapped around a tricky word! He'd got it stuck good and proper this time, and he went on calling meteors metaphors as if I'd never spoken, just so he wouldn't lose face. Like he did with his Winnifred rays.

But to get back to his secret. Although he was a

young bear, he had already suffered his first broken heart. He told me so himself. He put on his most superbly melancholic air; he twisted his muzzle around to give himself a more afflicted-looking profile; and he said to me with a sigh: "When she broke my heart..."

I had to pinch my lips tightly together to nip the smile in the bud that was already tickling my cheeks. You should never laugh at someone who is telling you about his first broken heart, not even if that someone is a little bear cub who hasn't been around long enough to have a broken tooth, let alone a broken heart.

"Was it a long time ago?" I asked with false candour.

He made a kind of arabesque in the air with his paw, as if to say: "Ah, Time...Time means nothing when you're in love."

No doubt about it, my Christopher Cartier was one precocious little bear. And he took himself so seriously, too. So seriously, in fact, that I found myself wondering how deep this love was, that could express itself in such pompous gestures. Because as soon as he saw how interested I was in his amorous adventures, he really started pouring it on: it was all Miss Weasel this and Miss Weasel that—his first love, I gathered, had been a member of the Weasel family. He had fallen in love with her, it seems, on the very day of the bear cubs' victory at the Battle of Hazelnut.

"The Battle of Hazelnut?" I asked.

Then his last name must come from...

But Christopher Cartier did not like jumping to conclusions before he even had time to tell the story. So I was treated to the whole epic, stanza by stanza, of the Hazelnut clan.

It all began one autumn, a long time ago. It had to be autumn, of course, because of the hazelnuts, and I didn't bother asking how anything could have happened to Bear a long time ago if he was barely twelve months old. An epic is an epic, and you have to swallow it whole. You can't go examining it too closely for common sense. And Bear, you will have noticed, was not one to quibble over a moon or two when he was in the middle of a good story.

So I held my tongue.

"Anyway," he went on, "it was autumn. The sky was clear and crisp and beautiful, and the nights were full of stars . . ."

I could tell already that he was stalling for time, trying to make up the story as he went along. He was soon on the right track, and after one big breath he poured out the whole song and dance, about how his line of descent extended from time impremordial, about the Polar Bear, the Panda Bear, the Kodiak Bear, the Brown Bear, the Black Bear, the Grey or Grizzly Bear, the Lesser Bear, the Great Bear, the Star Fish—"

"The Star Fish?"

"A distant cousin," he said, "on my mariternal side."

He'd say anything, would Bear. I didn't dare give him a lecture about how the relationship between stars and star fish was purely metaphorical, because the very word metaphor would have sent him flying right off the handle again.

Instead, I proceeded to get it straight from the horse's—pardon me, the bear's—mouth: the story of the Three Bears and their encounter with a little girl named Goldilocks, who walked right into the bears' house one day and gobbled up all their porridge. Bear even tried to tell me that the Baby Bear in the story had been none other than you-know-who—Christopher Cartier of Hazelnut, that's who.

"Speaking of hazelnuts," I ventured, trying to get him back on track.

That summer, according to Bear, had taken place the fiercest, the most Homeric battle ever fought in living bear-memory. It had involved the entire forest. Or the whole underbrush, anyway: the fluffy-tailed squirrels, who hid their hazelnuts in the hollows of their cheeks; the sharp-eared rabbits, who really preferred cabbages to hazelnuts but who signed on anyway so as not to be left out; the sabre-toothed beavers, who used hazelnut branches in their lodges and dams; the sleepy-eyed groundhogs, who hibernated on hazelnut-branch beds; and even the weasels, with their long, sleek bodies and their pointy snouts, who—

"Wait a minute," I cut in. "Weasels?"

Bear thought for a minute, then finally had to admit that because weasels were meat-eaters they were not terribly fond of hazelnuts. They had actually got caught up in the battle, he said, because of their cousins the ferrets, who are always ferreting about in other people's business. Now could he get on with the story?

As a matter of fact, Bear said, at the time the war in question was in question, the weasels and the bears weren't speaking to each other. They weren't sworn enemies or anything, but they weren't bosom buddies either. "It was a question of class," said Bear. "Weasels are common; bears are nobly born. Weasels are among the lower edge-alongs of society."

I was taken a bit aback by Bear's snobbishness, I must admit, and I began to wonder whether his claim to being a member of the aristocracy went back much farther than the famous Battle of Hazelnut. But on that score Christopher Cartier soon set me straight:

"One is nobly born at birth," he said, with his nose stuck up in the air.

He's right, I said to myself, bears are noble creatures, with or without hazelnuts.

"About the weasels," I prompted.

"Ah, yes," he continued, "the weasels." Now that he'd started the story he had to finish it. And finish it he did. Bear wasn't short on imagination or creativity. You could always count on him to recount his encounters with the Count of Monte Cristo, once he got started, inside out and backwards. He talked about his first love as Shakespeare talked about Romeo and Juliet, as Don Quixote talked about Dulcinea. He pined, he swooned, he crossed his heart and sighed at the moon, he lifted his paws to Heaven and swore, calling the flowers to witness, that never again would he allow his wanton eyes to settle on the weaker sex—

"Oh ho!" I cried. "One day out of the woods, still wet behind the ears, and already your mind is full of muck! The weaker sex indeed!"

But we'll leave that for now. He was, after all, still a little bear who had never been to school, and I couldn't get angry with him over a question of vocabulary.

"And then what?" I asked.

Then the two families had strongly opposed this impossible love between a bear and a weasel, and Bear had come down with a severe case of heartache.

At this point in his tale he began to touch me deeply. It was the first time that I felt he was telling the truth. Until then he had mostly been trying to impress me with a lot of sighs and swoons; now, all of a sudden, he really was remembering Miss Weasel, and missing her. He went on to tell me, without fuss and embellishings, without turning on all the machinery of classical tragedy, with nothing but the memory of a single happy moment in his life, about his poor little Weasel, who had been so cute in her white fur coat and so pretty with her saucy little snout already poking here and there—she was such a flirt, so unpredictable, that Bear laughed and cried in turns as he talked about her.

It was true: his heart really had been broken.

I took out a large checkered hankie and wiped his nose for him, then gently brought the subject back to hazelnuts: "Were there a lot of them?" I asked.

"A lot of what?"

"Hazelnuts."

He managed to pull himself together fairly quickly for someone whose heart had been so tragically broken. Like a cat landing on his feet. Little bears love life; they'll grasp at any pretext they can to shake off a fit of the blues. Bear stretched out his neck, cocked one eye, and opened his mouth to pick up his tale where he had left off.

"Hazelnuts," I reminded him. "Were there a lot of them?"

He swung his arms around in a wide circle that took in the whole world: "Like that," he said.

That was a lot of hazelnuts, all right. Certainly enough to be worth fighting for. And they were round and firm, the colour of hazel (not surprisingly), the most beautiful prize in the woods, and the most delicious.

"It was that fox who started it," he said.

Ah, it was the fox who started it; and all the time I thought foxes only ate chickens.

"Foxes will eat anything, as long as it's stolen."

He wasn't kind, was he, toward his fellow forest dwellers. "They're sneaky and treacherous and they'll attack you from behind when you're not looking."

32

Then came a sudden change of tune.

"But they're funny, though, which is why we let them fight with us."

That made sense. If you can have fun when you're fighting, you can tell yourself that you're only fighting for fun. I began to feel sorry for that poor little fox.

"How did he start it?" I asked.

Bear's face took on its angry look again, and his voice sounded very authoritative:

"Everyone was out taking the air one morning, as usual," he said, "all of us minding our own business. The lynx was chasing the fox who was hunting the marten who was sneaking up on the partridge who took off after the butterfly. . .the earth, in other words, was turning very much in its usual direction, which is to say in circles. Then the fox had to go and spoil everything. That particular morning the marten and the weasel weren't there because they were at a meeting to discuss a family matter. So the fox, who was hungry as a bear, went straight for the partridge."

"The villain!" I cried. "He went over their heads. That isn't done, is it?"

"It isn't done," repeated Bear, who seemed to like the sound of it. "But that's not all!"

"There's more!"

Not content with jumping up a rung in Nature's ladder, just to put some food on his table, the fox landed right smack dab in the middle of a heap of hazelnuts that the squirrels had squirreled away last autumn. That's when the fur really began to hit the fan. The squirrels were too small to take on the fox, so they jumped on the moles instead. The moles attacked the spiders, and the spiders took it out on the butterflies. Poor butterflies—feast or famine, they always seem to be the ones to get the dirty end of the stick.

But the squirrels weren't the only animals who were partial to hazelnuts. Don't forget the rabbits and the beavers and the groundhogs and the weasels and the martens, all of whom used some part of the hazelnut tree for goodness knows what. The whole kit and kaboodle got into the act, and, in less time than it took Bear to tell me about it, hackles were raised, feathers were ruffled, beaks and muzzles were clucking and miaowing and snorting and caterwauling and nipping and pecking, and before long a real battle royal was underway.

Except it wasn't really a battle royal, because the moose and the rest of the deer family stayed out of it, up on their hill, their antlers spread out against the horizon. They didn't even bother to look down their snooty snouts at the small fry scurrying about in the underbrush. The moose, as everyone knows, is the king of the forest, and kings don't go about getting mixed up in the petty affairs of their subjects.

Bear was almost beside himself with rage when he talked about the moose. "Who do they think they are, anyway?" he cried, "Those jumped-up parvenus! Kings of the forest, eh? Bears, I'll have them know, have been around a lot longer than mooses. Bears are older, stronger, and more intelligent—why do you think bears are so well known for their long memories? But those mooses just take themselves for granted."

He said "mooses" because he was angry, and when you're angry sometimes the old ways of saying things come skipping back to your tongue. Haven't you noticed how sometimes even famous poets use words that are old and generally thought to be no good anymore, but are usually the only ones that seem to sound right?

"I wish those mooses and deers and the whole

ungulating clan of them would sit right down on their own horns," he expanded, forgetting that deer don't have horns, they have antlers. But he had made his point: bears were the first lords of the forest. And that's why they had to take part in the battle whether they were interested in hazelnuts or not.

"So off we went, the whole family," said Bear.

On cross-examination it turned out that the sole representative of the bear clan at the ensuing Battle of Hazelnut was none other than you-guessed-it: Bear. Adult bears are not naturally war-like; they're not even naturally sociable. But bear cubs sure are. They love to argue, which is why they love being around other people.

Bear dove into the fray, head first.

"And you won the battle and returned the hazel-nuts to their rightful owners," I said.

But I had leapt to conclusions again, I'm afraid. It hadn't been as easy as all that. Wars have their rituals, you know, their rules, like any other game. We humans may have forgotten that, but the animals haven't. This was a clean war, fought for honour, dignity, family pride, faith, high principles, country, the unknown soldier, war for war's sake, not just for a bunch of old hazelnuts. It wasn't Bear's fault if, at the end of all that dignified fighting, the hazelnuts sort of ended up in the lap of...er, well...of Christopher Cartier, also known as Bear.

Not exactly in his lap, either. In fact, they had tumbled down and conked him on the head while the skunk was defending herself against the porcupine, who had just fired a broadside of quills into her never-mind-where. The shot seemed to have unleashed a tidal wave of springwater that came gushing down the gully with so much force that it was every man for himself. Bear, who was a touch slower, perhaps a tad more curious, and no doubt much braver than the others, took the whole shooting match full in the face. He only jumped back a little bit, but he came down on a stick that banged against a branch that shook the trunk of the oak tree in which the squirrels had hidden their cache of hazelnuts...

And that was how Bear carried off the spoils of war—receiving, in the process, the titles and privileges accorded to the first Lord Hazelnut.

V

*A*utumn was already well advanced one day when I caught Bear trying to civilize some of the local fishermen's sons. Until then he had been content with crushing the daisies, annoying the herons, and tweaking the beaks of the seagulls, larks, sawbills, and all the rest of the beach's flying squadrons. It was good fun, he confided, but it lacked a certain rotundity.

"A certain what?" I asked.

"Rotundity," he repeated solemnly.

That's when I remembered seeing him the evening before in my study, his snout buried in one of my books. It didn't take a genius to understand seagulls, he explained. Anyone who could fall off a log could understand a seagull. But since he had decided to enlarge his circle of acquaintances, he felt he had to broaden his vocabulary as well. And that's why he was devouring my dictionary. By chance his snout had stumbled on the word "rotundity," which had a good, solid sound to it and pleased him no end. He used it everywhere. Oranges had rotundity. Culture, certain pebbles, mountains, the Minister of Finance—in short, everything and everyone who was round or important displayed some degree of rotundity.

His relations with the shore birds, however, definitely lacked rotundity. He had decided to work his way up the social ladder.

You would have thought, wouldn't you, that the

obvious thing was to work his way up gradually, to go from seagulls and daisies to, say, household pets—dogs, cats, canaries, Woolworth's turtles, guinea pigs, goldfish, frogs, and other friends of children. Not Bear. He went straight for the children themselves. He had no sense of social order: he didn't know what was done and what was not done. Besides, he was in a hurry.

"Not a minute to lose," as he often told me.

He did everything in a hurry. He didn't walk, he galumphed. When he ate, he gobbled and gulped. He even snored quickly. He never did anything by halves that he could do by quarters. "Winter's on its way," he would say, "and I'll have plenty of time to sleep then."

I never paid too much attention to that last phrase because I guess I had stopped thinking of my friend Christopher Cartier as a bear. And I put it out of my mind completely when I saw how full of life he was, as if every day was his last on earth.

The fishermen's sons evidently saw things more clearly than I did. They followed Bear everywhere, from one adventure to the next. Every morning I'd see them go off together over the sand dunes and along the beach, threading their way through the tall grass, scrambling over piles of shells, clambering and jogging, slogging and splashing, generally making a mess of field and shore alike.

Ah, the good life!

But a demanding life, just the same. And full of responsibilities. Sand along the seashore usually contains hundreds of treasures, and you can't just leave treasures lying around to rot. And since the tide comes in and covers up these treasures at six o'clock in the morning, you have to get there during low tide. Mushrooms come out of their underground nests to wink at the rising sun as soon as the goblins and gnomes wake up, who use them for umbrellas, and if you're there you see them, if you're not, well. . .It's a tough life.

That's why Christopher Cartier, who proudly bore the names of North America's greatest explorers, wouldn't let anyone sleep in, but would lead his escort of children and dogs and frogs, to be joined outside by seagulls and sawbills and even, on good days, by crows, into the most secret and marvellous of worlds.

Of course, things didn't always run smoothly, and more than once I had to go down to straighten them out. Each time, naturally, it was Bear's fault. Bear might have been the most exuberant, the most dynamic, most fearless and peerless of knights, but he was also one of the scruffiest, nosiest, stubbornest, most impetuous, boastful and contentious little scamps on the whole East Coast.

For example, take his belief—which he maintained in direct opposition to the rest of the world, not to mention the laws of physics—that it was twice as easy to climb up a hill as it was to go down it. He based this theory on the fact that his fore legs were shorter than his hind legs, an anatomical arrangement that invariably caused him to roll head-first every time he tried walking downhill. He was careful to explain this theory to his friends and cohorts, who might otherwise have taken him for a clumsy oaf.

But most of the time I would let him work out his own problems, to teach him a lesson. Like the day he discovered bees. Bear had to learn that it isn't always the strongest who are right. He had a tendency to think he was right more often than was good for him, and if he had some foolish need to learn everything the hard way, well, at least he learned.

And that day he learned the difference between bees and wasps.

I know, I know, you might say that they come to pretty much the same thing, bees and wasps. They both belong in the flying/stinging category. Granted. But they are attracted by different things, and they sting in different places. And there are different subcategories too, and Bear would have been much better off if he'd known that when he first ran into our coastal bees, and not mistaken them for ordinary wasps. Bear, who was so particular about degrees of kinship between Polar Bears, the Great Bear, Star Fish and so on, had to go and get confused about wasps and bees! But don't forget, my friend Christopher was living at full speed, and he always insisted on getting straight to the essential point. It's a dubious theory, of course, as are all theories that deal with essential points: what is the essential point for one side isn't always the essential point for the other side.

The essential point if you're a bear cub, for example, might be to sniff for beechnuts under the big oaks in the forest on a cold afternoon in the fall; or to go fishing for trout with great swoops of your paw in the icy streams in spring; or to stick your nose into a hive of honey without paying attention to the bees that are there swarming about looking like wasps.

Unfortunately for Bear, the bees had all their essential points right there in the hive.

And that was that.

As a result, that autumn morning Bear came limping up to me. Worse than that, in fact: he came wriggling his backside like a toddler who has had an accident in his pants. I know, bears don't wear pants, so you have to look around for their accidents. But the kind of accident Bear had just had you didn't have to look around for. It was quite obvious.

"Dirty rotten sons of *boo*ers!" he shouted, hobbling on all fours toward his porch.

He had a dirty mouth, did Bear, I'd known that ever since I heard him holding forth that day in the underbrush. And I was just waiting for him to favour me with it. Favour me, did I say? Rub my nose in it, is more like it, with a gesture that was far more eloquent than words.

Once again I was torn between punishing him and laughing my head off. But you can't laugh at someone else's misfortune, can you? So I had to scold him.

"What have you done *this* time, Bear?" I asked. I let my eyes wander down to his little silk bottom and I had to force myself to keep a straight face: he had more dimples on him than a thimble.

He didn't answer me. He was too full of shame and anger and wounded pride. Instead he kept repeating "sons of *hoo*ers!" as if, by using such words, he felt some relief from the stingers that were burning his behind. I knew that the "hooers" in question were our neighbours the honeybees, who like to visit me at the lighthouse during daisy and wild-rose season.

"So you went poking about in their hive, did you?" I said in a tone that left no doubt about what I thought of little bear cubs who don't know their manners.

He raised his left eyebrow and lowered his right one, to make himself look both sorry and angry. It gave him two ways to escape: Bear had the knack of never putting all his eggs in one basket.

Anyway, after his adventure with the bees I think he really became aware of how mixed-up his feelings were, because if he had an angry heart he certainly had a sorry and contrite behind. That's why he rubbed his bottom with one paw and waved the other one furiously in the air, soothing his heart of all the injuries it had suffered:

"Rung of a chair on Main Street!" he shouted, imagining that he was inventing the most horrible swear-words ever spoken. "Lamp in the chancel of the clock tower with the sponge in its holy water!"

I doubted very much if he understood what he was saying, and I let him swear himself out of breath. His vocabulary, I thought, would run out at about the same time as the stinging stopped.

All things considered, the adventure with the bees had its good side. I was sure that Bear wouldn't try to steal honey from a hive again without first making friends with its occupants. At least, I thought, he had learned that much.

His apprenticeship, however, had just begun. I remember the first time he saw a pumpkin...Poor Bear! I must say in his defence, though, that his first pumpkin *was* an extra big one, and that this was his first autumn—his first autumn out of the woods, anyway.

It was Indian summer, and the leaves were all yellow and red, and Bear was so busy searching for acorns in the furrows made by the farmers' ploughs that watching him made me feel exhausted. I kept calling out to him: "Bear, don't be silly, come back here now and listen to me."

Then he stopped.

Oh, I thought, so obedient all of a sudden?

But it wasn't that (I should have known): Bear had just met his first pumpkin. His fur bristled, his hind feet came up in front of his fore feet, and he shouted:

"It's a metaphor!"

He'd mixed up metaphor and meteor again, but I knew what he meant.

"It's a pumpkin, Bear of Hazelnut. A fall fruit."

He seemed disappointed and excited at the same time: full of apprehension because the pumpkin was nearly as big as a castle, and full of expectation because the pumpkin was of a most appealing shape. Here was one thing, at last, that had no lack of rotundity.

"Pumpkin," he repeated, rolling the new word around between his tongue and the roof of his mouth, as if he could taste it.

He was something of a poet, was Bear, and he liked to feel sounds splashing out of his throat like water out of a gargoyle. More than once I surprised him arguing with himself using more and more complicated words, persistently rolling syllables that had no "r" in them, and twanging words through his nose that had no "n."

"It's for eating?" he asked suddenly, his nose already twitching at the thought of food.

"Of course. It's best as jam."

"Aha!"

Poor Bear! Whatever possessed me to put the idea of jam into his head? As if bears know how to make jam. You must never put useless ideas into people's heads, my father used to say, because it's cruel to give people a peek at inaccessible treasures. My only excuse was that, since being forced to hitch my life onto this forest reject, I had forgotten where he came from and had started treating him, on certain days, as a friend and fellow human being.

Each to his own, I told myself. Nature is wiser than her creatures, and who are we to meddle in her affairs?

My reflections on the matter had reached that point, at least, when one morning, as I was gnashing my teeth over a particularly complex sentence, I suddenly smelled what seemed to be burnt caramel coming up from below my tower. I tumbled down the spiral staircase four steps at a time, and ended up at the bottom nose to muzzle with a most curious and unidentifiable object struggling up from the bottom of my biggest copper cooking pot.

Needless to say, I was surprised.

It was, of course, Chef Christopher Cartier, all decked out in a white paper bag for a chef's hat, a white tablecloth for an apron that wrapped around his waist about eight times, his chin dripping, his ears drooping, waxed paper sticking to his tail, and his paws stuck in a puddle of thick yellow syrup that was already giving off a pretty pungent perfume.

"Bear!" I cried. "What are you *doing* down here?"

He looked up at me with miserable eyes, trying to find some way out of this sticky situation. He was a prisoner of his own pumpkin jam, and it would take him the rest of his life to lick himself clean.

He consoled himself a little by presenting me with a new friend: Jack O'Lantern, who had a ready smile and eyes that couldn't stop winking at me. That was another nice thing about Bear: no matter how much he wanted jam, he couldn't bring himself to slice that pumpkin down the middle, scoop the seeds out of its skull, then cut it up into cute little cubes. He preferred to do it his way, by cutting little holes in the shell to make a face, round as a full moon, with crossed eyes, a flat nose, crescent-shaped ears, and a mouth that never stopped smiling. That way he could have his pumpkin and eat it too, a very Bear-like solution.

Of course, he then tried to claim that he had invented Hallowe'en, the little faker. Don't you believe it. Hallowe'en goes way back to the very beginning of Time. Bear just discovered it by chance one day while fooling around with some copper pots, trying to make jam. He'd probably tell you he invented jam, too, if he thought of it.

VI

*I*t was very mild that day, even though we were well into autumn. It was as if Indian summer would never tire of dragging its beige-and-ochre-striped tail over our hillsides. I took advantage of the fine weather by going for long walks along the beach, very early in the morning, sucking in deep lungfuls of salty air and looking for signs of the first snowfall. I still hadn't made up my mind to close the lighthouse for the winter; I kept putting it off and putting it off, telling myself that as long as the last goose still hadn't left for the south . . .

Between you and me, I don't think I was really waiting for the geese to leave. I think I was waiting for a certain bear cub, whom I had adopted or who had adopted me, and for whom I now felt responsible. I couldn't just send him back to the woods, but neither could I bring him with me to the city. There was still too much country in him.

In the meantime, I waited. And waited. I don't know what I was waiting for; maybe a miracle, maybe for the hand of fate to come down and point me in a certain direction. Who knows? It was as if I thought life could take care of itself without my having to raise so much as a little finger to help it along. I know it was a dangerous kind of assumption to make, that I was misunderstanding the roles of Nature and Chance. But never mind. For the moment I went out each morning to collect my purple and blue pebbles, and to take Bear for short rides between the shoals in my rickety old rowboat.

When I say I "took Bear for rides," that's just a manner of speaking, of course. It was Bear who took me, with his "Turn here!" and "Turn there!" and "Left!" and "To port!" and "Steady on starboard!" and "Hard to north-north-west!"

We sailed far out to the open sea, just the two of us, scudding into the troughs of huge waves, skirting the off-shore islands, tacking around icebergs and plow-ing through pack ice. We waved to passing white whales and porpoises, and came home an hour later giddy and drunk on the finest dreams of adventure and conquest.

I let myself be rocked to sleep by the ocean, and by Bear's hoarse, staccato voice. He really thought he was Christopher Cartier, you know, and he carried on a constant monologue with the gulls and herons:

"Hey! You sawbills!" he shouted. "We need a figurehead on this man-of-war. Come on down and perch on our bowsprit!"

The fact that our rowboat had no such thing as a bowsprit didn't faze him in the least. That was just Bear's way of being hospitable. He was inviting his friends over for a visit. Unless...

Unless Bear, with his bear's-eye view of the world—he was still a little cub, after all—had a truer perspective on the people and things around him than I did. He saw them in their true dimensions: bigger than life. There is no guarantee that a tree, say, is big and that an ant is little. An ant may be smaller than me, but it's bigger than a flea. And go ask the clouds if a tree is tall!

Bear viewed the world through his own eyes, and his own eyes were quite close to the ground. You can see how he might take my little rowboat for a huge man-of-war. Or my pebbles for rubies.

"What did you call those pebbles?" I asked him the first time I heard him say the word.

"Not pebbles," he insisted. "Rubies!" And he stamped his four paws on the wet sand so clumsily that he fell down. He made me think of my own mistake, when I thought my pebbles were rubies that had washed down from the Gaspé.

"Okay, okay, Bear," I said. "You don't have to go into such a rage about rubies...I mean pebbles."

"Rubies," he mumbled through his beard—or rather through the fur on his chin—in order to have the final word on the subject.

And he believed it, too. I'm convinced of it to this day. The pebbles along my stretch of coastline were his friends; he loved them, and when you love something it becomes, well, sort of transparent. You can see inside it. Bear looked into my pebbles as if they were prisms, and just like that they became rubies. And before I knew it I was calling them rubies myself.

It's a bit like the story of the daisies: you remember I told you how the first night Bear came to my lighthouse he tried to bed down among the daisies? Well, don't think that that was the end of their friendship.

Today, looking back on that autumn with Bear after nearly a year, I think I can honestly say that I understand his character and his mentality. Not that it's all that difficult to understand: Bear was unique. He was one of a kind within his species. Each time I tried to take him apart, to examine all the different pieces that went together to make Bear, I always ended up confronted by something that was all of a piece. Everything about him was Bear, it was as simple as that. He had a Bear laugh, a Bear walk, a Bear hug, a Bear bluster, and Bear fantasies. Exactly as if, I swear, every hair in his silky fur was struggling against Nature to make a personality, a constitution, a physiognomy that was absolutely, quintessentially Bear.

I suppose he is what philosophers would call a "person true unto himself."

And that's why he was so fiercely loyal to his friends. To the daisies, for example.

This friendship between the daisies and Bear was quite surprising, considering what a bad start it had got off to. You remember that first day, when they said to him: "Didn't anyone ever teach you some manners!" You remember that? But I think way down deep inside, that kind of frankness didn't bother Bear at all. And they did make him feel useful and wanted. Daisies really need a lot of care if they are to survive in the sand, exposed to all those salt winds and high tides.

How many people do *you* know who would even give a thought to the health and welfare of a daisy? How many would stoop over and straighten a bent stalk, or wipe off a petal after the wind has been at it, or bring them a drink of water on a dry, hot day? I don't know anyone but Bear who would put up stakes for them, and surround them with moss and clover and dandelions, to make them feel more at home.

In fact, all Bear needed to be the absolutely perfect friend of daisies was—patience. I don't know how often I had to say to him:

"Bear, look out! Don't yank on those stems. They'll come up on their own. Let Nature take her own time!"

But the temptation was always too great for him. He grabbed the poor daisies with his two front paws, planted his hind paws in the ground, and yanked. Poor daisies! They came out of their beds all anyhow. And worse, they came out too soon, unable to hold on to the sand with their roots. Then Bear would come over all penitent and try to stick them back in the ground.

And do you know what? With all that planting and unplanting and transplanting and retransplanting, and in spite of all his gaucheries and impatience, Bear actually made those daisies stronger, and ended up by turning them into real daisies after all.

And without my being aware of just how it happened, one day I noticed that my lighthouse was beginning to look like a real lighthouse again, once and for all.

Yes, even my lighthouse!

I'm not saying it suddenly started lighting up the coast for lost sailors. I'm not going that far. A former lighthouse or an out-of-service lighthouse can't just start lighting up the coast for lost sailors. But as Bear pointed out, anything that sails to sea can be called a sailor. And gulls sail to sea, and larks and herons and albatrosses and alcatrazes, and storks when they carry newborn babies in their long beaks. . .And the whole fleet needs some place to put in for repairs, to have a rest, to find shelter or to stretch their sea-legs from time to time. Seabirds need guides just as much as seamen do, and navigators, and that's just where my lighthouse can come in handy. That's how it can fulfil its destiny as a lighthouse.

I slept soundly that night, when I realized that thanks to Bear I had become the Keeper of My Own Lighthouse. But then, when I realized that soon I'd have to shut it up for the winter—winter always follows close on the heels of Indian summer—I felt a sharp pain in the general vicinity of my heart.

But the next day, when I saw that autumn was still dragging its yellow and ochre tail, I postponed putting on the storm windows, cleaning up the yard, storing away in the shed all the garden tools and fishing gear that are usually found scattered about the base of a lighthouse. And I went for a walk along the dried-up salt flats that border the beach, aiming great swooping soccer kicks at the piles of leaves that we say are dead but that are only pretending to be dead.

The weather really was superb—it was like a reprieve. I guess that was what prompted Bear, who somehow knew the school calendar better than all the kindergarten-to-grade-sixers put together, to leap out from under his porch in the early hours and charge down to the beach, filling the air with his shouts: "Come on, come on, wake up, get out of your nests! It's a bea-*yoo*-tee-full day!"

And the children tumbled out of their houses in groups of twos and threes, pulling on their boots and scarves and sweaters, hopping into life on one foot, rigged out and ready for the great adventure of a brand new day!

"Hurry up! Quick! Let's go—the tide waits for no one!"

Bear leapt into the air, shouting until he was out of breath, his four paws barely touching the ground and his mouth so wide open it looked like he was trying to sink his teeth into every minute that flew by.

And so the game would start. Every day they would invent a new one, but I had already discovered, through careful observation, that all the games played along our coast were variations on one main theme. Hide-and-seek, blind-man's-buff, cat-and-mouse— they all had a lot in common and were played more or less according to the same rules. So much of my own childhood had been spent chasing after mice and kings of the castle that I eventually came to think of mice and kings as being pretty much the same thing: something to run after whenever they crossed my path.

Children today can't be much different, even though they *are* more intelligent, more highly evolved beings. Now they hardly set foot in school before they can multiply 248,027 by 39,411, and rhyme off on their fingers that the capital of Afghanistan is Kaboul and its inhabitants are called Afghans. But as for games...

On this famous day in late autumn, when I watched Bear rallying the whole countryside to play on the beach, I was astonished to discover that in five generations nothing much had changed. I say five generations because that's as far as I know; two generations before mine, two after mine, and mine:

$$2+2+1=5$$

I can therefore assure the gathered assembly that five generations of Acadians have played the same games following the same rules and making the same sounds. I know of few other traditions that have lasted so long.

That day they played "Bear."

Don't you find that exciting, the idea of playing "Bear" with a real live Bear? That makes it more than a game, it makes it...what? Is there really any difference? Bear or no Bear, you're still playing "Bear." You hide a bear under a pile of leaves, and all the other players circle around the pile singing, "Who's afraid of the big bad bear, the big bad bear, the big bad bear," as they close in closer and closer to the pile, closer and closer, until they're almost touching it, and then they *are* touching it, and then—*ROAR!!*—

out pops the bear making a terrible growling roaring sound, and he leaps onto the first player he can catch and gobbles him up! Oh, it's a great game.

The only problem was that Bear always wanted to be the bear, which seems natural at first. But when you come to think of it, and if you're playing by the rules, the person who gets gobbled up is supposed to become the bear, and the bear is the really fun part of the game. He's the star of the show. It was a real problem, then, and the children didn't know how to deal with it.

So of course I had to step in. Again.

I explained to Bear that the game, which has been played by children since the beginning of Time...

"Like Hallowe'en," he said.

"Yes, like Hallowe'en."

And I went on to say that the game "Bear" had certain rules and regulations that symbolized certain things. Man's struggle against the forces of Nature, for example.

"I *am* the forces of Nature," Bear replied.

"Yes, Bear, I know, but..."

I began to get a little exasperated:

"...but these forces of Nature are wild and uncontrollable. They are symbols of chaos, and..."

Well, if you think he took *that* lying down. Bear? Chaotic? Bear, who every morning arranged his spoonfuls of acorns and hazelnuts into neat, ordered, identical piles; who always ate the same amount every day at the same time—every hour on the hour—who every morning ran along the same beach chasing after the same herons with the same enthusiasm; who...

"Okay, Bear, okay! I didn't mean that *you* were chaotic. I was talking about symbols. And a symbol is an image of something *else*, like a metaphor..."

Oh, why did I have to say metaphor! Once again he

mixed up metaphor with meteor, and started yelling about falling stars.

I don't know how I ever would have got out of that one if Nature herself—whom I had just been maligning so meanly—hadn't come to my rescue. Bear, who had his nose pointed up to the sky to look for falling meteors, suddenly felt something else falling from the sky. It landed on the tip of his muzzle: it was snow.

Winter had closed in on us, all of a sudden, without a word of warning.

Quickly I snatched Bear up in my arms and ran with him to the porch.

He was yawning before I even got there.

VII

*C*hristopher Cartier of Hazelnut slept like a bear.

But poor me!

Just imagine my predicament. I knew enough about the habits of bears to know that this one was going to sleep all winter, blast him. When I looked between the slats I could see him under my porch, all curled up like a ball of wool, his muzzle buried in his paws.

But what was *I* supposed to do? Oh, I'm the first to admit that it was my own fault. Well, maybe the second—if Bear was awake he'd be the first to point it out for me. I know just what he'd say, too: "When the time comes to close up your lighthouse, you close up your lighthouse. If you don't, that's *your* look-out!"

Easy enough to say after the fact. But winter doesn't usually drop down on you like a bandit from a tree, without so much as a by-your-leave.

That year the snow came down harder and harder, covering up the rubies, the leaves, the seashells, even the little rowboat that I had luckily had enough sense to pull up out of the water. Only the daisies had been smart enough to see winter coming: for several weeks they had been sound asleep on their mossy mattress, and bit by bit the moss had swallowed them up. Just as bears sleep above ground on beds of branches and dried leaves, daisies sleep underground, covered up by their own gardens!

But me?

I couldn't just up and leave, could I? Save myself and abandon Bear, who, I had to admit, didn't seem to be too concerned about what I did. He was sleeping peacefully, the sleep of the just, twitching his tail from time to time as if to tell me: "Don't go yet, I'll be up as soon as it's spring."

Well, I *knew* that! But I also knew that he wouldn't need me or anything else during the winter. A bear eats his fill from spring to fall, accumulating so much fat and so many vitamins that he needs all winter to sleep them off. It's called hibernating.

And that's what Bear was doing now: hibernating.

I could have gone back to the city; there was still time. I could have shut the shutters, turned off the porch light, locked the storm doors and gone back to the city as I did every other year. I could have come back to the coast early in spring, before Bear woke up, and he never would have known I'd been gone. It was all still possible.

But there was that flick of his tail, that twitch of his ear. He *would* just raise his muzzle from its furry pillow, just a touch, just enough to let me know he was alive.

Very well, then, Bear. I'll wait.

And so I waited.

It was the first winter I'd ever spent in the lighthouse. I didn't hibernate, though. I'm not a bear.

I may not have hibernated, but I came close to it. Let me explain. A lighthouse is not like an ordinary house; it has no street in front of it, no number, no yard to share with the house next door. No house next door, in fact. It's all by itself, except for the ocean—stuck in the sand like a fencepost, surrounded by boats, some seaweed, and the fishermen's nets.

Life in a lighthouse doesn't follow routines and timetables like life in the city, either, or even in the village. Farmers can't just farm whenever they feel like it, for example; they have to farm when the land tells them to, or else the land will fight them every step of the way, and the farmer will never get anywhere. And in the city—let's not even talk about the city. The city is up to here in rules and regulations and routines and schedules and timetables and red lights and green lights and one-ways and no-left-turns and up-escalators and down-escalators and neon lights that come on at all hours of the day and night, automatically.

In a lighthouse—a real lighthouse, that is—nothing is automatic. Everything is done by hand, and whenever you get around to it.

What freedom, eh?

And it was just as well, too, especially after I introduced a bear cub into my life. Now don't tell me that he came on his own steam, that I hadn't actually asked him to follow me home. I could have stopped him, and sent him back. If I had wanted to I could have...but, well, I guess I didn't dare. You remember how little he was? And how ...funny?

And he didn't really change my life that much. I was still in charge. I got up when I wanted to, I ate when I felt hungry, I went for walks whenever I was in the mood...except for when Bear dragged me out onto the shore or among the dunes to look for buried treasure. But it was my idea, for example, to share my hazelnuts with him, and my pumpkin jam. He ate up half the jam, of course, and *all* the hazelnuts, but what could I have done about that? He was so little, you see, and so...funny.

As for the lighthouse, he didn't change any of *its* routines. It still had its pebbles and its seagulls and its larks and its field daisies transplanted into sand daisies—except that now the daisies had hardened off and taken root, the gulls were tame and spoke to us often, and the pebbles had somehow turned into rubies. That's all.

My lighthouse hadn't changed much at all, except that now it was a real lighthouse. And I hadn't changed much either, except that now I was spending the winter in my real lighthouse, and it was the most beautiful winter of my life. That's all.

I never knew how lovely winter can be by the ocean. For one thing, the ocean itself can freeze over. Not for long, mind you, and not every day, but when it gets really cold, twenty or thirty below zero—oh yes, in our neck of the woods January can hit you with forty below—so when it gets really cold and the sky is clear, the ocean sort of stiffens up, and then it stops moving altogether. And when the tide comes in, the ice breaks up, and the sea carries off the huge ice-pans that look like icebergs, and then the next day at low tide it freezes again, and once more I've got a fine, white, hard patio at the foot of my lighthouse—a patio that stretches as far as the eye can see.

Bear would have been beside himself at the prospect of going on an arctic expedition into that infinite white world. But arctic expeditions are for polar bears, those big white brutes of the Far North. And just as I was no Eskimo, Bear was no polar bear. That's why I didn't try to turn my lighthouse into an igloo, or wake up Bear, who was slumbering so soundly under my porch.

Besides, by letting him sleep until spring I wouldn't be missing anything. I had a good idea that as soon as he woke up he'd begin telling me about all the dreams he'd had during the winter. Bear lived in dreams all the time anyway, whether he was asleep or awake, so you can imagine the visions that would be dancing through his little bear-brain over the course of a whole winter of sleeping. He would have been capable of rebuilding the Temple of Jerusalem single-handed, if he had only known that it had been pulled down. He could have reconquered Rome, or Babylon, or turned the bumble bees into humble bees and brought home their hives full of honey on his shield. He was capable of anything, was Bear, when he took to dreaming. And since that's what hibernating is for, I had to prepare myself for anything.

And I thought I *was* prepared for anything.

But I wasn't prepared for what happened one fine morning when the weather had cleared, in early April.

I had opened all four windows in my bedroom to find out whether the wind that morning was blowing from the north, east, south, or west, and I had determined that it was coming from the south-south-west. A dry, sweet wind, which was fine by me. It meant that sometime that day my sand dunes would be ploughed into at least fifty-six mighty rivers that would carry the rest of the melting snow tumbling out to sea. I could relax, do some writing. . .

"Holy snappin' arseholes, I'm hungry! By the Lord Liftin', am I *ever* hungry! I'm hungry as a bear, I'm hungry, hungry, *hungry!*"

I was thunderstruck.

Down below, on my own doorstep, was a crowd of the noisiest, nosiest, most boisterous creatures on the coast, all scurrying back and forth, each trying to convince the next that he was the greatest thing since sliced bread. And right in the middle of all the bedevilment, his four paws and even his tail bobbing above everyone's heads, was Bear.

Once more I tumbled down the stairs and ran out onto the beach. It was really him, Christopher Cartier, Lord Hazelnut, badgering everyone, yapping at them, getting his former friends and playmates all fired up to begin life afresh.

"Bear!" I shouted. "Bear, you're awake!"

Was he *ever* awake! Of that, at least, there could be no doubt. I'd never seen anyone as awake as Bear was. He was so wide awake that I bet he never wanted to close his eyes again. Every muscle in his body was humming with life, and he was rolling every "r" and twanging every "n" he knew. And at the heart of this flood of words was one refrain: "I'm hu-u-nnnng-reeee!"

I got the picture: he was hungry. And for once I had to agree: when you haven't eaten all winter, you're likely to be hungry in the spring. I ran inside to ransack my cupboard for anything a hungry bear might like to eat—in other words, everything that was in it.

"Not the paper, Bear—don't eat the box!"

He gobbled and slobbered, he slurped and he burped. "Yum, yum," he said at last, smacking his lips.

I suddenly remembered the brouhaha that had been tearing up the beach a few minutes ago, and I asked Bear what it had all been about.

"It wasn't about anything," he said. "Everyone's just telling fibs."

Well, I thought, every fib can hide a bit of truth. And the truth I discovered about Bear that day was that, despite his long incubation, he was still the same old Bear, still up to his old tricks: in order not to feel left behind by his friends, who hadn't had to take a winter-long nap, Bear had invented a whole series of adventures for himself to equal theirs. He may have dreamed some of them, and maybe he even thought they were true. But they were a good way to shut the yap of the first silly goose who started talking about his winter vacation in Florida, or one of the fishermen's sons who felt like telling someone about his snowball fights.

"You wanna know what I did?" Bear asked, suddenly inspired. "I visited some of my relatives."

"Oh?"

The others' admiration for Bear was unanimous. He was back where he belonged. How was it down there? Where had he been? Who had he seen? They wanted to know everything.

And Bear told them everything, and then some.

The more they went "Aaah!" the more he laid it on. What started out as a simple visit to his family was extended to include a few aunts and uncles, then his mariternal cousins the Star Fish, then on to his second cousins of the first degree, the Black Bears, then on to the second degree and so on until he had arrived at the very roots of beardom, the august trunk from which had sprouted all the various saplings—the Great Bear himself.

"The stars!"

Oh sure, he had travelled among the stars, sauntered along the Milky Way, hitched a ride on a shooting star, tweaked Betelgeuse's beard in passing, waved to his cousin Ursus Minor. In short, he had gone on a long voyage of self-discovery, right back to where he came from.

I hid my smile behind my hand: I didn't want to spoil the day for such a great raconteur and digger-up of long-lost relatives. But I said to myself:

"Yes, some day he *will* have to go back to where he came from."

VIII

*B*ut that would come later: for now, Bear was more interested in different kinds of roots. As I watched him scraping the sand in front of his porch with his four paws, I asked him what he was doing.

"Where are they?" he asked in reply.

"Who?"

"The daisies."

Good old Bear. He was more than capable of making those daisies rise up out of their nests before their time. Once he put his mind to something, there was no stopping him.

"Bear, you know you're supposed to let things be, let Nature and Life work at their own speed. The daisies will come up when the sun's first warm rays hit them in June. When you wait for something you have to...well, wait."

"Wait, wait, wait," he grumbled. "Always wait." It was the hardest thing anyone could tell him to do. Sometimes I think he must have been born ahead of his time.

"We can console ourselves with mushrooms, then," he said to me one day in May—that long, long month that was keeping him away from his beloved daisies.

"Mushrooms!" I said. "They're even worse. They don't come out until September, and even then only if they really feel like it. Why, I've seen them stay out of sight right into October, especially during leap years."

"Leaf years?" he burbled, as if he suspected a trap. But curiosity got the better of him: "Why don't mushrooms like leaf years?"

I had no idea—I had just said that about leap years without paying much attention to what I was saying. I suppose I was thinking that because the extra day in a leap year falls on February 29, it makes an extra day of winter, and so it would be a bad year for mushrooms. It was just one of those things you say, like making a summer out of one swallow. Then I realized that *that* didn't make much sense, either. "You see, one swallow *doesn't* make a summer," I muttered under my breath, looking up at the sky.

Bear, thank goodness, had developed the habit of leaping from one topic to another at a very early age, and so he forgot about his leaf years and fastened his attention on my poor swallow, out of which he made one of the best summers it had ever been my pleasure to spend on the coast.

We had become fast friends, Bear and I. And each day, while the wild geese filled the sky and dandelions exploded in the fields, and polliwogs paraded through the streams, we went for long walks among the dunes and in the woods, discovering the world and conquering Time.

Time! Time was our worst enemy.

One day I said to Bear, trying not to sound too philosophical: "Time is the only thing that comes between spring and winter, day and night, and a child and an old man."

He looked at me, his eyes big and round and full of twinkling stars.

"Let's put a stop to it," he said, clenching his fists.

"Stop it? Stop Time?"

"Yes, yes, let's trap noon right at 12 o'clock and not let it out again until twilight."

And he was off again, very proud of his new word "twilight," which he pronounced like a grown-up, without swallowing one slippery syllable or tripping over the two high "i"s. I, on the other hand, was just as proud to see Bear was exploring the world from the inside for a change.

For a bear, it's child's play to catch flies or caplin or even swallows. But Time! Just try catching Time on the fly! It takes Bear, Lord Hazelnut, to even entertain such a notion—and to go so far as to speak of it out loud! We've all had dreams of stopping Time in its tracks for a moment or two, I suppose. But Bear wasn't dreaming. He was loaded for bear!

"You won't catch me!" he was saying to Time. "It's me who'll trap you!"

And he leapt up, pirouetted on his tiptoes, and shadow-boxed in mid-air with the winds of Time. In the mornings he would dash out from under my porch and charge straight for the horizon—it didn't matter which horizon, because in our part of the country the sun rises on all four sides at the same time.

And the rumpus would begin. All I could hear was:

"Don't move!"

"Gotcha!"

"You're dead!"

But Time, alas, didn't die. It never dies. It's the other way around: Time kills us. I tried to explain that to Bear, slowly, without making a big tragedy out of it—there's no need to make a big tragedy out of something as simple and natural as Life.

He listened for about three seconds, then cut in to let me know that he understood.

"So it's Life that's the enemy. It's Life we've got to conk on the head."

He hadn't understood much, had he? I started again. It didn't do any good to conk anything on the head, I said patiently, or to kick anything in the butt. "Let things alone, Bear. Everything will happen all by itself—day will follow night, summer will follow winter, bears will follow bear cubs. . ."

He blinked his eyes three or four times, and for a moment I thought the sun was in them. Then he raised his paw as if he was going to scratch his nose. I even thought I saw him turn his ears toward the shore, where the gulls were cawing, as if he wanted to hear some other voice than the voice of reason. Which made me understand that he had understood me all too well.

He said nothing more that day, letting the hours slip quietly by, one after the other, along their well-worn path. At dusk, just before going off to bed, he came up to me and nestled his big, furry head in the crook of my elbow, and sighed:

"When *will* I be a big bear?"

I put my arms around him and gave him a big bear hug. And spoke to him very softly, so that he wouldn't leave off watching the moon, which had raised its forehead and one eye above the horizon out over the sea. We all become big bears sooner or later, I said. I'd gone through it myself; it was a Law of Nature, Life was like that. And, all things considered, it wasn't so very bad.

I could feel the resistance deep down inside him, as if he were afraid of suddenly losing all his baby fur and being left naked until his big-bear fur grew in.

"But what about the seagulls?" he asked. "They won't play with me when I'm a big bear. And the beehives will be too small for my muzzle, and Miss Weasel won't even recognize me anymore!"

Poor Bear. He was really down in the dumps. I didn't try to soothe him with fancy stories about the horrors of a prolonged childhood or any twaddle of that sort. He wouldn't have believed me anyway. And besides, I knew that deep down he was still a very brave and adventurous explorer, and that in spite of his fear of the unknown he was brimming with curiosity and impatience to find out what was around that big, new corner.

"And you have to *be* big to do big things," I said.

"I'm going to be *very* big, aren't I?" he said, cheering up remarkably. "Just like my great-great-grandfather, the Great Bear.

Very good, Bear, I thought; well said. If you've got that far to go, you might as well get off on the right foot.

"And there's lots of time, you know," I told him. "You could even get some sleep first. It's not as if you're leaving tomorrow or anything."

I could have saved my breath: he was asleep already.

He must have dreamed all night about growing up, because early the next morning, when he came back to life, he patted his ears, his muzzle, his tail, and his little silky bottom, and seemed quite surprised to find that everything was unchanged. Nothing had fallen off, got bigger, or grown fatter. His voice may have deepened a tiny bit, but it still wasn't gruff enough to frighten a sparrow.

So little had changed, in fact, that Bear promptly forgot all about his longing and fear of the night before. And *hop!* it was down to the shore and into the dunes as usual. Time didn't feel like stopping? That was Time's look-out. He was going to live Life in the fast lane. A nibble here, a gulp there, he'd gobble up Time and stuff his heart and kidneys with enough memories to last him the rest of his days.

One day I caught himself rubbing my ear, the way Bear did.

It made me think.

By inflating every single second of Life, I said to myself, you end up making Time bigger. And when it's bigger, not only is it more manageable, but you get more of it! Bear was right! He hadn't killed Time; he had swallowed it whole. That way he knew he'd never run out of it. Everywhere he went, for the rest of his Life, he could take his Time, tucked away deep in the treasure-chest where he kept his heart.

"When I'm a big bear I'll still be Bear, won't I?" he asked me one day.

"Of course," I told him. "You'll be Bear all your life, even when you're all grown up. I promise."

It was an easy promise to make, because if I knew anything I knew that even as a big brown bear in our deepest, darkest forest, Christopher Cartier of Hazelnut would have hidden under his fur, locked up somewhere between his heart and his backside, the bawlingest, braggingest, fearlessest, thoughtlessest, hare-brainedest, smartest, most adorable, most incomparable little bear cub that ever lived: Bear.

He could rest assured of that!

IX

*S*o Time passed, and I thought Bear had forgotten all about his quarrel with the hours that flew by so quickly and couldn't be stopped.

But don't *you* believe it! Bear? Forget about something once he'd made his mind up to catch it? Not on your life! Time had become Bear's Public Enemy Number One, his favourite sparring partner. They played no ordinary game, those two—not hide-and-seek or blind-man's-buff. I never did figure out the rules they played by, either, though I thought I recognized most of the elements: the challenge, the chase, the counting one-to-ten, the ready-or-not-here-I-come.

Then one day Bear came to me with a question, which he asked in a voice that had gone down one more notch in his throat:

"How much Time is left?"

The question caught me right off guard. It nearly bowled me over.

"How much Time is left before the daisies come back?" he wanted to know.

The daisies! Whew! I breathed a little easier.

"Pretty soon, now," I told him. "Two or three days, maybe more, maybe less."

He gave me such a broad grin that all his teeth flashed in the sunlight for the whole world to see. Then he shouted:

"I won! I won!"

And he *had* won. He had beaten Time at its own game, by pretending to be going along with it. He had figured out that Time—which, as everyone knows, can be very cruel when it wants to be—is also the only thing that can make the daisies return every year to the same spot.

And he knew the spot. He could see them under there, I swear, and he whispered quietly to them that he had dreamed all winter long of their soft, white petals.

As he waited, I watched him ramble more and more often among the spruces, and tamaracks, and the white poplars in my back yard, stopping every now and then to sniff their bark and examine their roots. Spring was filling him with more and more life every day. It was also making him more pensive, more dreamy—however much he tried to hide it from me.

So dreamy was he, in fact, that the day when he finally saw a tiny yellow button pushing its way up through the ground just outside his porch, struggling mightily to stretch out its petals, Bear just held his breath and watched, as if after all his rehearsing for this moment he had forgotten his lines.

"There's your daisy, Bear," I urged him. "Don't you even want to say hello?"

He squatted down on his haunches, sniffed at the flower, and looked up at me in astonishment.

"It's a pretty darn small flower," he said.

I suggested we go for a walk in the woods.

"It won't be long before the ferns come out, too," I said.

"Fiddleheads!"

He loved fiddleheads, mainly because they had such a musical name. They're called fiddleheads because the tips of them are curled up like the head of a violin, and because every time you see them you feel like singing. Bear also liked them because they taste absolutely delicious.

So without closing up the lighthouse, without so much as a backward glance at the seaweed, the nets, the boats, the gulls, the rubies, and the fishermen's sons who were still chasing each other across the sand dunes, Bear and I set off hand-in-paw along the quiet path that led into the forest.

We sang "A la claire fontaine" together, stripping the tops off the young dogwood shoots as we went. "Do you remember your first pumpkin, Bear. . .and your first battle with the bees . . . and the first time you went hunting for herons. . ."

On his long legs the Heron, with his long bill. . .

And we laughed and cried together, remembering the good old days.

And they *had* been good old days, all things considered. We had both learned so much, had pressed so many pretty rose petals between the pages of our family photo album. . .Roses are red, violets are blue, pumpkin jam is sweet. . .

Suddenly he stopped. Had all our reminiscing suddenly reminded him of his beloved Miss Weasel and his other friends of long ago? Or was it the smell of straw and pussy willows that filled the forest path so early in June?

Whatever it was, Bear stood frozen to the spot, as if on his guard. He was listening for something. He made me feel nervous, and I started to ask him—

"Shhhh!" he said.

I shushed.

All of a sudden his left ear perked up, then the right, then his tail. Then, in a flash, kicking his heels up behind his neck, he took off.

"Bear! Bear! Where are you going?"

I tried to keep up with him, but it was no use. He was running very fast and very smoothly, his strong legs adjusting to the rough terrain—it was, after all, his natural habitat. I stumbled and staggered, banged my head on a low-hanging branch, caught my arms and legs in the bushes, panted, sweated, and cursed myself for ever thinking of taking Bear for a walk in these woods.

Then he stopped, just like that. He turned his head right around, as if trying to unscrew it from his shoulders, and gave me a rather peculiar look.

"When I was young," he said, "this is where I used to hide my nuts."

When he was young! Imagine that! I had to smile at my naïve little bear cub, whose fur was still as soft as eiderdown, whose little paws were so light they hardly left a mark on the moss when he pranced around like a darling little idiot. A bear cub who couldn't frighten a seagull, and yet who talked about his childhood as if it was hidden way back in the murky recesses of Time. Time, I said to myself for the nth time, was a strange, strange thing.

Time. But it had been me and no one else who had told him about Time, and Life, and how things change from day to day, and each day they change a little faster...

"This is where you used to hide your nuts, eh?" I said. "From who?"

"From the squirrels, and the rabbits, and the field mice, and the gophers, and the foxes who used to hide *theirs* just over there."

"Oh, so you knew where everyone hid their nuts?"

"Everyone knew where everyone hid their nuts."

"Then...why hide them at all?"

He gave me a long look, the kind of look you give someone who asks how come 2+2+1=5.

But what I *did* understand, though, was that I still had a lot to understand. By coming back to his old stomping grounds, Bear had become more Bear-like than ever; which meant that he had reverted to the least logical logic in the world, perceiving everything through his own two, Hazelnutty, bear-cubby eyes that hadn't had enough time yet to take very much in.

Not enough time?

I was ashamed of myself for having had such a stupid thought. Had I forgotten about all those ancestors of his, the millions upon millions of bears who had roamed these woods over the past centuries? Forest creatures have been foraging for food from the land and the rivers and the trees since the beginning of Time, and what was left over they've been hiding out of instinct, out of an instinct for tradition. Because without traditions we lose a part of ourselves. Is a monkey who doesn't monkey around still a monkey? And a ferret who doesn't ferret about, or a badger who doesn't badger anyone, how are they different from field mice or groundhogs?

In his own woods, Bear knew lots of things. As I was quickly discovering. All the science I could teach him from my porch or in the tower of my lighthouse couldn't hold a candle to the trick his nostrils had of zeroing in on a cache of nuts hidden deep in the forest. It occurred to me that if Picasso's genius was in his eyes, and Mozart's was in his ears, then it could be said that Bear's genius was in his nose. Everyone's doesn't have to be in their brains.

"Look! Look!"

Bear had just recognized a scent—a fox's, probably,

because he started to growl: "That's him, that's that stinker, that traitor—he's invading my territory again. Watch me get him!"

And he was off again like one possessed, even more ecstatic than he had been on the beach or among the sand dunes. I could see there was no catching up to him—once he was in the woods he was much faster than I was. So I sat down on a stump—if I couldn't catch Bear, at least I could catch my breath.

Which was too bad, because it meant that Bear and I parted without ever saying goodbye. I tried not to think about that, but something caught in my throat about the size of a pumpkin, and it wouldn't go down. I thought about climbing the twenty-six steps of my tower every morning, of looking out to sea, watching the rise and fall of the waves, shouting to the seagulls to shut up and stop bothering the herons, of adding to my collection of purple and blue pebbles, of staking the daisies while I waited for. . .

Waited. I could wait a long time—perhaps forever—before finding another friend who would so fill up my dunes and my lighthouse with his cries of pure joy, who would play such tricks on everyone along the coast. Why, I could wait. . .

But what's this? A column of ants, snaking past my feet? A headless, tailless procession, winding its way along the ground, weaving through last year's leaves? I give my head a shake and they're still there, so I join the line, I'm in it, I can hear the chattering and badgering already, the thirty-five-cent words and the fifty-cent sentences, the pompous phrases, the devilish uproar that gets louder and louder as I draw near—a screeching, miaowing, croaking, chirping, yelping, chattering, cooing, warbling. . .cacophony!

And there he is, back in his old underbrush, right in the middle of an admiring circle of rabbits and badgers and gophers and squirrels and skunks and foxes, all present and recounting their own misadventures, contradicting themselves and their neighbours, noses to the wind, fur at the ready, ears and tails drawing arabesques in the air.

Bear has come home.

I lean over to whisper a quick word of goodbye, and I hear him addressing his friends with the most bombastic blarney you can imagine; pure moonshine:

"The country's all yellow and humpy," he is saying, "with whole piles of honey all along the beaches, and rubies that shine brighter than daisies, who have to eat salty marshgrass because the seagulls pick up the seashells by the seashore on Sundays, and they bother the boats that have to go way out to sea, way out past the moon that keeps coming up every night and then goes down again every morning behind the shimmering leaves that are only pretending to be dead, and then the moon opens her eyes wide wide wide and her nostrils and her mouth and then she's called a pumpkin, which makes a very nice honey jam . . ."

At the mention of honey, Bear pauses to lick his little bear-lips gluttonously, giving me enough time to look down at the ground, find my procession of ants, and leave the underbrush the way I had come, on tiptoe.

And I never went back there again.

I crossed the fields to my lighthouse, cutting through the cornfield and the hayfield and the dune grass, my feet heavy and my heart floating on a sea of honey and pumpkin jam. I walked without raising my eyes because I didn't want to see the seagulls again, or the rubies, or to notice that I was crossing the salt flats. What was I going to tell the daisies when they came up? I could already hear them asking for Bear as soon as they opened their petals: "Where's our gardener?" they would say. And I could see the bees reinforcing their hive in preparation for Bear's attack on their honey, and I could hear the herons asking each other nervously why the reef was suddenly so quiet—too quiet—and I knew I wouldn't have the heart to face the fishermen's sons as they tumbled out onto the sand in the morning to look for buried treasure. I didn't think I could ever face anyone on the coast again.

"Hurry up! Get a move on—there's no time to lose!"

My head shot up like a rocket.

There on the beach was the same old brouhaha, with the noonday sun shining down with its old smile, the honey-yellow sand just dripping and the rubies winking in the sunlight at the seashells, who turned all pink with pleasure. And the seagulls calling to the larks, who shouted at the children to get into the boats, they were going out to sea to catch the moon and make some jam, because it was time to water the daisies and they couldn't keep them waiting!

I trudged up the steps of my tower, whistling "Au clair de la lune" and "A la claire fontaine," hauling a bucket of soapy water so I could polish my lamps. Because I now knew that sometime soon I'd be lighting them up every night to show the seagulls and the larks where they were supposed to be going, and before I went to sleep each night I'd wave up at the Great Bear, who looks so funny up there with his broad Jack O'Lantern smile.

Don't you think?

—January 30, 1981
Montreal

76